MAKING TRACKS WITH MICHAEL

Bike off into strange and unknown parts. Climb into the
sidecar of a BMW and careen around our land with Michael
J. Doonesbury, with Mark, a computer drop-out, with
Joanie Caucus, a thirty-nine-year-old runaway housewife,
and with other transients who believe that America has
yet to be definitively discovered.

GARRY TRUDEAU, twenty-six, is a loner. He knows no
home, and his only companion is an old collie.

Call Me When You Find America

a *Doonesbury* book by G. B. Trudeau

BANTAM BOOKS

TORONTO · NEW YORK · LONDON

CALL ME WHEN YOU FIND AMERICA

*A Bantam Book / published by arrangement with
Holt, Rinehart and Winston*

PRINTING HISTORY

Holt, Rinehart and Winston edition / October 1973
2nd printing . . . . . . March 1974   4th printing . . . September 1974
3rd printing . . . . May 1974   5th printing . . . . April 1975

Bantam edition / February 1976

Published simultaneously in the United States and Canada

Bantam Books are published by Bantam Books, Inc. Its trade-
mark, consisting of the words "Bantam Books" and the por-
trayal of a bantam, is registered in the United States Patent
Office and in other countries. Marca Registrada. Bantam
Books, Inc., 666 Fifth Avenue, New York, New York 10019.

PRINTED IN THE UNITED STATES OF AMERICA

0 9 8 7 6 5 4 3 2 1

IT IS A SOLEMN MOMENT HERE IN WATTS.

THE PRESIDENT CARRIES A WREATH, A WREATH WHICH HONORS THE MANY BRAVE MEN WHO FOUGHT IN THE WATTS RIOTS OF 1965.

THE PARTY IS NOW APPROACHING THE BURNED-OUT STOREFRONT... THE LOCAL DRUM CORPS PLAYS A ROLL..

.. AND FINALLY,... THE PRESIDENT PLACES THE WREATH ON THE TOMB OF THE UNKNOWN INNOCENT BYSTANDER.

YES. MR. SEMPLE.

MR. PRESIDENT, LAST NIGHT, AFTER YOU PARACHUTED THROUGH THE CAPITOL SKYLIGHTS, YOU MADE AN ADDRESS TO CONGRESS WHICH MANY SENATORS THOUGHT PATRONIZING. ANY COMMENT?

MR. SEMPLE, I AM AWARE OF THIS CRITICISM, AND I FEEL IT UNFAIR. I TRIED TO DESCRIBE MY TRIP TO WATTS WITH CARE AND TACT.

BUT, SIR, DO YOU THINK "A GLORIOUS SAFARI" WAS THE WORDING YOU WERE AFTER?

HONEY, I FINALLY FIGURED OUT HOW TWO FINE PEOPLE LIKE US ENDED UP WITH A LOUSE LIKE MARK!

..OL' FRED SIMPSON'S WIFE HAD A BABY SAME DAY AS YOU— YOU KNOW, TED, WHO GREW UP TO BE A FINE SCHOLAR. WELL, I FIGURE SOMEWHERE ALONG THE LINE THE BABIES WERE SWITCHED! THAT'S GOT TO BE IT!

HOW DO YOU FEEL ABOUT THAT THEORY, MOM?

23

31

WE SURE WERE SURPRISED TO SEE YOU DOWN ON THE FLOOR, ZONKER, WHAT'RE YOU DOING IN MIAMI?

I CAME DOWN WITH MOM! SHE'S A DELEGATE THIS YEAR..

I DIDN'T KNOW THAT!

SURE! SHE'S PUSHING FOR McCLOSKEY NOW, BUT ON THE FIRST BALLOT, SHE NOMINATED ME!

WHAT? YOU?

I WAS A "FAVORITE SON" CANDIDATE.

WELL, WE'VE GOT TO GET BACK ON THE ROAD, ZONKER.

I SURE HATE TO GO BEFORE ALL THE DELEGATES ACTUALLY LEAVE. SOMETHING IMPORTANT MIGHT HAPPEN AND I'LL MISS IT.

MR. CHAIRMAN, THE DELEGATION FROM RHODE ISLAND REQUESTS PERMISSION TO SEND OUT FOR SOME PIZZA!

I'M OFF.

TAKE CARE.

SO THIS IS YOUR FIRST VISIT TO SAN FRANCISCO, EH, PILGRIM?

YUP... SAY, ARE THOSE GIRLS DANCING UP THERE REALLY CO-EDS?

WHAT?

YOUR SIGN OUTSIDE! IT SAID "BEAUTIFUL, EXCITING CO-EDS."

OH,...YEAH! SURE! THEY'RE CO-EDS! *SUZIE*, THE BLONDE THERE, IS A CUM LAUDE FROM WELLESLEY, AND *DORIS* IS A PHYSICS MAJOR AT STANFORD, AND *TIGER-LIPS*, THE ONE WITH THE LEGS, SHE'S MATRICULATING AT YALE THIS FALL.

WHY? YOU A COLLEGE MAN?

MS. CAUCUS—IF YOU DON'T MIND A PERSONAL QUESTION, WHEN DID YOU FIRST START HAVING DIFFICULTIES WITH YOUR HUSBAND CLINTON?

WELL, MIKE, IT'S DIFFICULT TO PINPOINT IT, BUT I GUESS IT MIGHT HAVE BEEN ONE NIGHT LAST SUMMER, WHEN HIS BOWLING BUDDIES CAME TO DINNER...

AT THE END OF THE MEAL, ONE OF HIS FRIENDS COMPLIMENTED ME ON MY FRENCH FRIES. CLINTON LEANED BACK IN HIS CHAIR, AND SAID WITH A BIG, STUPID GRIN, "MY WIFE, I THINK I'LL KEEP HER!"

I BROKE HIS NOSE.

GOTTA LETTER FROM MIKE HERE, ZONKER...

WELL, FOR LAND SAKE, BOY, READ IT!

"DEAR FRIENDS: BY THE TIME YOU GET THIS, MARK AND I WILL BE IN CHICAGO. WE EXPECT TO MAKE IT BACK TO WALDEN BY EARLY NEXT WEEK.

"WE ARE BRINGING WITH US A BEAUTIFUL, SENSITIVE, BUT CONFUSED LADY NAMED JOANIE, WHOM WE PICKED UP IN DENVER. WE BEFRIENDED HER BECAUSE SHE HAD NO ONE ELSE TO TURN TO DURING A MOMENT OF CRISIS.

"SO IT'S NOT WHAT YOU THINK."

WHEW.

HELLO, ZONKER!

HI, MS. CAUCUS. MIKE SAYS YOU'RE GONNA BE STAYING AND HELPING WITH ALL THE COOKING 'TIL YOU FIND A JOB.

THAT'S RIGHT, ZONKER!

WELL, THIS HERE'S A LITTLE WELCOME PRESENT. A BOUQUET OF WHEAT I PICKED FROM MY WHEAT PATCH!

WHY... ZONKER... WHAT A LOVELY, **LOVELY** THING FOR YOU TO DO... THANK YOU SO MUCH...

I'LL DO ANYTHING TO GET FED PROPERLY.

GENTLEMEN, AS THE PRESIDENT'S CAMPAIGN MANAGER, IT HAS BECOME MORE AND MORE CLEAR TO ME THAT ONLY **RADICALS** WILL BE VOTING FOR THE OPPOSITION!

IN FACT, I AM MOST CONFIDENT THAT COME NOVEMBER, WE'LL BE ABLE TO SEE JUST WHO DOES AND WHO DOES NOT LOVE HIS COUNTRY!!... YES, MR. RATHER...

MR. MACGREGOR, RECENTLY THERE HAS BEEN SOME TALK THAT SOME DECENT FOLKS MIGHT NOT SUPPORT MR. NIXON BUT ACTUALLY VOTE FOR SENATOR McGOVERN.

THAT'S A VICIOUS LIE!!

BUT SIR..

B.D., I'M DEEPLY CONCERNED ABOUT ALL THESE BOMBING REPORTS. I WONDER IF WE COULD DISCUSS IT.

DISCUSS IT?! WHAT'S TO DISCUSS? THE U.S. IS BOMBING NORTH 'NAM TO CONTAIN COMMUNIST AGGRESSION. IT'S THAT SIMPLE.

YEAH, BUT THEY'RE NOT HITTING JUST MILITARY TARGETS. THEY'RE ALSO BOMBING DIKES AND SCHOOLS AND HOSPITALS AND DEFENSELESS HAMLETS!

BUT THEY'RE NOT DOING IT ON PURPOSE!

OH...WELL, THAT'S DIFFERENT..

AAARGG!! AIEEE!!

ZONKER, DEAR! DID YOU HAVE ANOTHER BAD DREAM?

IT WAS ANOTHER MARK SPITZ NIGHTMARE, MS. CAUCUS! ONLY MUCH MORE REAL! PRACTICALLY LIKE HE WAS HERE IN MY ROOM!

LOOK! HE WAS HERE IN MY ROOM! HE LEFT ONE OF HIS GOLD MEDALS!

ZONKER, THIS IS YOUR BELT.

AND THE SHEETS! THEY SMELL OF CHLORINE!

MS. CAUCUS!!

OH, ZONKER, NOT MARK SPITZ AGAIN!

BIG AS LIFE, MS. CAUCUS! HE WAS RIGHT HERE IN THIS VERY ROOM! I SWEAR IT!

I SAW HIM WITH MY OWN EYES! HE WAS LEANING OVER ME, LOOKING IN MY MOUTH AND COUNTING MY CAVITIES!

GBTrudeau

GOOD NIGHT, DEAR.

YOU BELIEVE ME, DON'T YOU, MIKE?

SURE, ZONK.

I GOT THROUGH LAST NIGHT WITH A GOOD, SOUND SLEEP, MIKE. NO MORE MARK SPITZ DREAMS.

I JUST CAN'T UNDERSTAND WHAT THE PROBLEM WAS. EVERYTIME I ROLLED OVER, THERE HE WAS, DOING DEEP BREATHING EXERCISES AT THE FOOT OF MY BED.

WEIRD! MAN, I'M GLAD **THAT** ORDEAL IS OVER.

WELL, I'M HAPPY YOU'VE GOT IT UNDER CONTROL.

HI THERE!

HELLO, MS. CAUCUS? AH... THIS IS REVEREND SCOT SLOAN SPEAKING. THE UNIVERSITY EPISCOPALIAN CHAPLAIN?..

...YES, THAT'S RIGHT, WITH THE BEARD... SAY, I WAS WONDERING IF YOU WOULD LIKE TO STEP OUT WITH ME TOMORROW SOMETIME... YES?..

YES?

SHE SAID YES!

SAY GOODBYE, REV.

I HEARD FROM PHRED TODAY. HE WANTS ME TO SPEND VACATION OVER IN THE 'NAM. I THINK I JUST MIGHT GO...

I KNOW WHAT YOU'RE GONNA SAY: "PINKOS ARE BAD NEWS!" BUT PHRED'S DIFFERENT FROM MOST OF THEM TYPES. HE OFTEN DRINKS BEER, AND HE LIKES CHUCK BERRY RECORDS.

AND WHILE I DETEST HIS POLITICS, YOU GOTTA ADMIRE HIS DEDICATION. HE'S BEEN WORKING FOR THE V.C. FOR A LONG TIME! PHRED'S NO COMMIE-COME-LATELY, YOU KNOW!

UH-HUH.

OR AM I JUST RATIONALIZING?

UH-HUH.

THAT THERE, MY BOY, IS ONE OF VIETNAM'S WORLD-FAMOUS REFUGEE CAMPS. DESTITUTION AS FAR AS THE EYE CAN SEE!

HI, PHAM! HOW YA DOIN', LEE!... HI, NGYEN, HOW'S THE WIFE?... HI, YA, PEEWEE.

PEEWEE?

HEY! I SMELL RICE SOUP. THERE'S ONLY **ONE** LADY REFUGEE WHO COOKS RICE SOUP LIKE THAT!

WHO'S THAT?

VENERABLE MOM!

111

GOOD
MORNING, DAD.

WAS THAT
REMARK
REALLY
NECESSARY?

SORRY.

SAY, DAD, DID I TELL YOU THAT ZONKER TOOK OVER FOR B.D. IN THE CHAMPIONSHIP PLAYOFF LAST WEEK?

IT WAS THE FUNNIEST GAME I THINK I'VE EVER SEEN. ZONKER MADE EIGHT FUMBLES AND THREW SIXTEEN INTERCEPTIONS! WHEN THE COACH FINALLY TOOK HIM OUT, THE SCORE WAS 85-0! HEEHEE! CAN YOU BELIEVE IT, 85-0! HA, HA, HA! HO! HO!

REALLY GOT A KICK OUT OF THAT STORY, DIDN'T YOU, DAD?